Disney · PIXAR
THE GOOD DINOSAUR

This edition published by Parragon Books Ltd in 2015

Parragon Books Ltd
Chartist House
15–17 Trim Street
Bath BA1 1HA, UK
www.parragon.com

ISBN 978-1-4748-2697-6

Printed in China

Disney · PIXAR

THE GOOD DINOSAUR

Apatosaurus Activities

PaRragon

Bath · New York · Cologne · Melbourne · Delhi
Hong Kong · Shenzhen · Singapore · Amsterdam

Meet Arlo!

Arlo is a type of dinosaur called an Apatosaurus. He lives with his family on a farm, where he is afraid of everything! But Arlo goes on an incredible journey that will change him forever....

Name: Arlo   **Age:** 10

Dino Type: Apatosaurus   **Best Friend:** Spot

What do you like most about Arlo? Write it below.

....

....

....

....

....

Baby Arlo!

Arlo started life as a tiny dinosaur baby.
Here he is in his egg. Colour him in!

Scrambled eggs!

Which one of these three dinosaur eggs was Arlo hatched from? Follow the path to find out the answer, then colour in the young dinosaur!

Odd dino out

These pictures of Arlo may all look the same, but one is different from the others. Can you circle the odd one out?

Answer on page 47

Shady characters!

Match each of these tough T. rexes to their shadow!

Nash

Butch

Ramsey

1

2

3

Answers on page 47

Memory game

Look carefully at this picture for 30 seconds and then cover it up with a piece of paper. Now see if you can answer the questions below.

1. **How many dinosaurs are there in the picture?**
   a) One, b) Five, c) Eight

2. **What are the dinosaurs watching in the sky?**
   a) An asteroid, b) A spaceship, c) A star

3. **Which of these things is also in the picture?**
   a) A house, b) A tree, c) A mountain

4. **What time of day do you think it is in the picture?**
   a) Night, b) Afternoon, c) Morning

Answers on page 47

9

Meet Spot!

Spot is a little boy who has been living in the wilderness all by himself. He behaves more like a dog than a human, but he knows how to survive! Colour in this picture of Spot hanging from a tree.

Into the wild

Follow the directions to help Arlo find his way through the wilderness to the farm.

START HERE

1. Go **EAST** five squares
2. Head **NORTH** two squares
3. Move **WEST** three squares
4. Go **SOUTH** one square

Mark the spot with an '**X**' when you've found it!

Answer on page 47

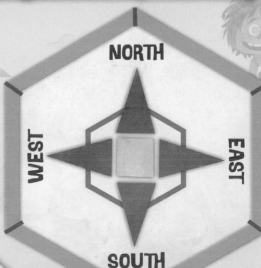

NORTH
WEST
EAST
SOUTH

Dino dreams

Arlo is lost in the wilderness. He's tired and hungry and daydreaming about food! Draw his dream then colour him in.

Words of wisdom

How many three-letter words can you make from the letters that appear in what Buck is saying below?

I AM AN APATOSAURUS AND ARLO'S BROTHER, BUCK!

Here are two to start you off. See if you can make three more!

MAN

....

TAP

....

....

....

....

Bug hunt!

Yuck! Spot is searching for big, juicy bugs to eat! Can you help him find a way through this maze to catch one?

START

Gotcha!

Arlo and Spot meet a family of T. rexes and enjoy a night around the campfire. Can you find six differences between the two pictures below?

Spot it!

Answers on page 47

Forrest time!

Copy this picture of Forrest Woodbush into the empty frame on the opposite page. Draw one frame at a time to make it easier — if you're feeling really creative, you can even add extra animals to his horns!

When you've finished drawing, colour in the pictures!

Going to pieces!

Can you work out where each of the missing pieces fits into the jigsaw puzzle? Draw lines to show where they all go.

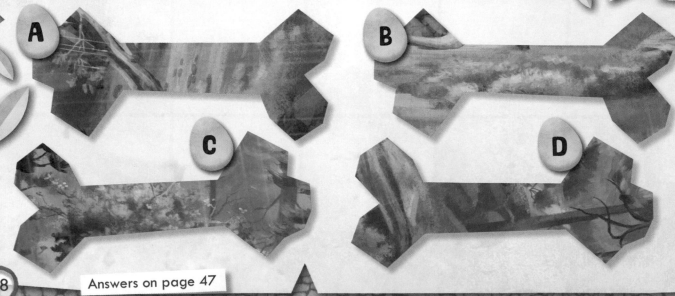

Answers on page 47

Who's there?

Spot has landed on something — but what is it? Join the dots to reveal the answer, then colour in the picture.

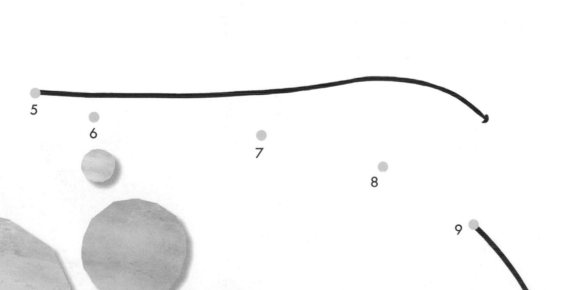

Answer on page 47

Terror in the sky!

Pterodactyls are flying overhead! Count how many there are and write your answer below.

One of them is carrying something. See if you can 'spot' what it is and draw a circle around it.

Answers on page 47

Meet Butch!

Name: Butch
Dino Type: T. rex **Job:** Rancher
Likes: Fighting crocs and raptors!
Dislikes: Losing his herd

What do you think the 'T' in 'T. rex' stands for? Put a tick next to the right answer.

- ◯ Tiny
- ◯ Twinkletoes
- ◯ Trouble
- ◯ Tyrannosaurus

Answer on page 47

Rancher round-up!

Try playing this fun game with your friends.
Who will be the first to find Butch's lost longhorns?

HOW TO PLAY:

- This is a game for two players or more. You will need a dice to throw and some coins to use as counters.
- Take it in turn to roll the dice and move around the board from one hoof-print to another.
- If you land on a hoof-print with writing on it, you must follow the instructions!
- The first one to find the longhorns is the winner of the game.

GOOD LUCK, RANCHERS!

START

1

2 You stop for a rest. Miss a go!

3

4 You lose the trail and end up in a swamp! Miss two throws.

5 You can see the herd. Hurry forward two spaces!

6

7

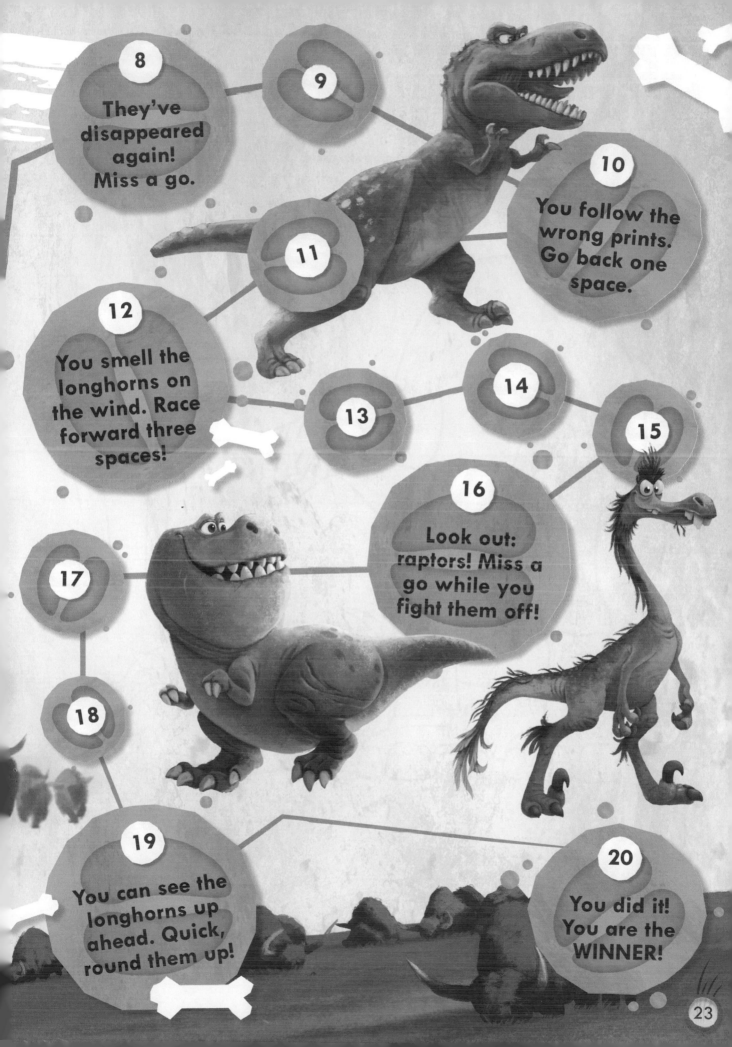

8 They've disappeared again! Miss a go.

9

10 You follow the wrong prints. Go back one space.

11

12 You smell the longhorns on the wind. Race forward three spaces!

13

14

15

16 Look out: raptors! Miss a go while you fight them off!

17

18

19 You can see the longhorns up ahead. Quick, round them up!

20 You did it! You are the WINNER!

Gopher it!

When Arlo and Spot meet gophers in the wilderness, Spot teaches his new friend how to make the critters pop out of their holes! Colour in this hilarious picture!

Before Arlo meets Spot, he imagines the little critter to be a huge monster. Can you draw a monster from your own imagination?

creepy critter

Now try giving your **monster** a friendly pet name!

....

Double dino!

Use the picture of Arlo to help you copy the colours so you have two pictures of Arlo!

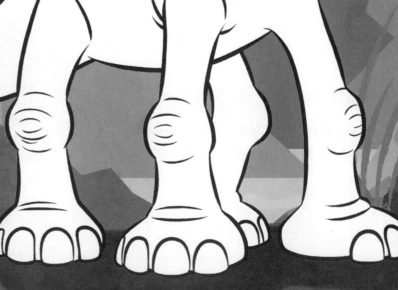

Up close!

Take a look at these close-up pictures.
Can you work out which character is in each
one and write their names in the boxes?

2

1

Write the names in the boxes!

3

Now look in a mirror and draw part
of yourself close up. You could draw
your ear, your nose or maybe your chin!
Remember to write your name under
the picture.

Answers on page 47

Spotting Spot

How many times does SPOT appear in the wordsearch below? Look across, up, down and diagonally.

S	A	E	S	Q	A
A	P	S	P	O	T
S	O	O	O	T	U
P	B	E	T	R	B
O	P	I	F	D	N
T	W	S	P	O	T

Design a dinosaur!

Henry and Ida's egg has hatched — but who's inside? Draw your own baby dinosaur inside the egg then colour in the picture.

Wild word!

Which of these creatures does Arlo not meet on his adventures? Circle the odd one out.

LONGHORN

HUMAN

T. REX

GOPHER

PTERODACTYL

ELEPHANT

RAPTOR

BIRD

Answer on page 47

Help Spot through the maze to his new family!

spot's new home

Answer on page 47

START

FINISH

Fossil Fun!

Create your own dinosaur fossils with this quick and easy recipe!

WHAT YOU'LL NEED:

- Four cups of flour
- One cup of salt
- Two cups of water
- Paints
- Lots of plastic toy dinosaurs!

WHAT TO DO:

1. Ask an adult to help you mix the flour, salt and water to create 'salt dough'. Then roll out the dough so it's about 1 cm thick.

2. Use one of the cups to cut the dough into circles. Now take your dinosaurs and press one into each of the dough discs.

3. Carefully take out all the dinosaurs — each one will leave a different dino shape in the dough!

4. Ask an adult to bake the dough circles for one hour at 180°C.

5. Once the circles are out of the oven, leave them to cool for 30 minutes. Get your paints ready....

6. Now paint your crumbly dinosaur fossils any colour you like!

Go wild!

Arlo and Spot love to howl at the moon when they are sad. Colour in this picture of them going wild!

Not Nash?

One of these pictures of Nash is not the same as all the others. Can you work out which one is different and circle it?

A

B

C

D

E

Answer on page 48

Catch the Longhorn!

Which path should Arlo take to catch the longhorn and avoid the raptors?

Answer on page 48

1

2

3

4

36

When Arlo sees the wilderness for the first time, he can't believe his eyes! Draw the view from the mountaintop — be as imaginative as you can!

Top of the World

Cowboy colour

Butch will do anything to protect
his longhorns from rustlers. Colour him in!

Spot's Lunch

Spot is hungry and is thinking about some nice juicy bugs. Draw some bugs for Spot!

Dinosaur quiz

How much do you know about *The Good Dinosaur*?
Find out by taking this epic quiz....

1. What's the name of Arlo's brother?

a Rock

b Rick

c Buck

2. What kind of insect does Arlo see in the field?

a Beetles

b Ladybirds

c Fireflies

3. Which one of these dinosaurs is Arlo's sister?

 a

 b

 c

 d

4. Who steals Butch's longhorns?

a Vultures **b** Raptors

c Humans

5. What does Arlo decide to call his little friend, the critter?

a Fido **b** Rex **c** Spot

6. What do Arlo and Spot fall down during the storm?

a A waterfall **b** A drain **c** A hole

7. Who does Spot go to live with at the end of the story?

a The Pterodactyls **b** A family of humans

c Arlo on his farm

Answers on page 48

How did you do in the quiz?

Write your score here:

The pet collector

Arlo meets Forrest Woodbush who loves collecting animals. How many can you count living on the dinosaur's horns?

Write the total number of animals here

Answer on page 48

Family sudoku

Can you help Henry complete the grid of his family below? Ida, Libby, Buck and Arlo should all appear once in each row and column. Draw them or write their names in the blank squares.

Answers on page 48

Swept away!

These two pictures of Arlo may look the same, but there are six differences between them. Can you find them all?

Answers on page 48

Spot might have caught a **bug** or a **lizard** – or even a **dinosaur!**

What's Spot got?

Spot loves to hunt anything that moves.
What has he caught in this picture?
You decide by finishing off the drawing!

Make your mark

Arlo's Poppa always told him it was important to make your mark.
Write your name in the space below.

Use this alphabet to help you with the letters

A B C D E F G H I
J K L M N O P Q R
S T U V W X Y Z

I,

....

....

**have made my mark by finishing
this book of Apatosaurus Activities!**

Answers

Page 6

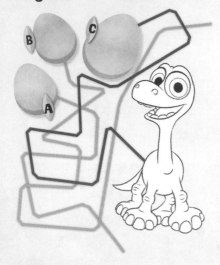

Page 7
Picture 3 is the odd one out.

Page 8
BUTCH = 1
RAMSEY = 2
NASH = 3

Page 9
b) Five
a) An asteroid
b) A tree
a) Night

Page 11

Page 14

Page 15

Page 18

Page 19
Spot has landed on Arlo.

Page 20
There are 8 pterodactyls. One of them is carrying Spot!

Page 21
Tyrannosaurus

Page 27
1) Arlo
2) Ramsey
3) Spot

Page 28
5 times

Page 30
ELEPHANT

Page 31

Page 35
E

Page 36
Path 4

Page 40–41
1. c) Buck
2. c) Fireflies
3. b
4. b) Raptors
5. c) Spot
6. a) A waterfall
7. b) A family of humans

Page 42
There are 30 animals.

Page 43

Page 44